For Dawn and Elizabeth. xx.

This book was first published in 1990 by Princess House
an imprint of Studio Editions Ltd
Princess House, 50 Eastcastle Street
London W1N 7AP, England

World Copyright, Text & Illustrations © Princess House, 1990

Text written by Claire Nielson

ISBN 1 85170 338 1

Printed and bound Hungary

CHESTER THE MOUSE
LOOK AND FIND BOOK

ILLUSTRATED BY JANE HARVEY

PRINCESS HOUSE

LONDON

"What fun, here's a jigsaw!"
Says Chester, the Mouse,
"Please help me find pieces
With knobs, like this house.
As soon as you see the
Red knob you will know
Just which is the right piece,
And where it should go.
There's a cow and a donkey,
A cat for the house,
What's that in the corner?
Like me, it's a mouse!
A goat, bull and rabbit,
A pig round and fat,
A farmer, a scarecrow,
Each wearing a hat.
A frog and a turkey,
A tractor, a cart,
Together we'll find them,
So, come on, let's start!"

Mouse

From his hole Chester peeps
And what does he see?
Now he squeaks, "Here's a mouse,
It's shaped just like me".

How many mice can you see on the wall?

One mouse, two, three, four, that's all.

Frog

Chester's chasing a frog
While keeping afloat,
With a toothbrush for paddle,
A soap-dish for boat.

Count all the frogs along the wall,

One, two, three, do you think that's all?

Tractor

Chester's happy to drive,
And his tractor's just fine,
But perhaps he should know
What is tied to his line!

Can you count all the trees from the left to the right?

Don't miss one or two that are just out of sight.

Goose

Do you think Chester's harder
To find than the piece?
Can you spot that red knob,
On one of the geese?

How many geese on the shelf so tall?

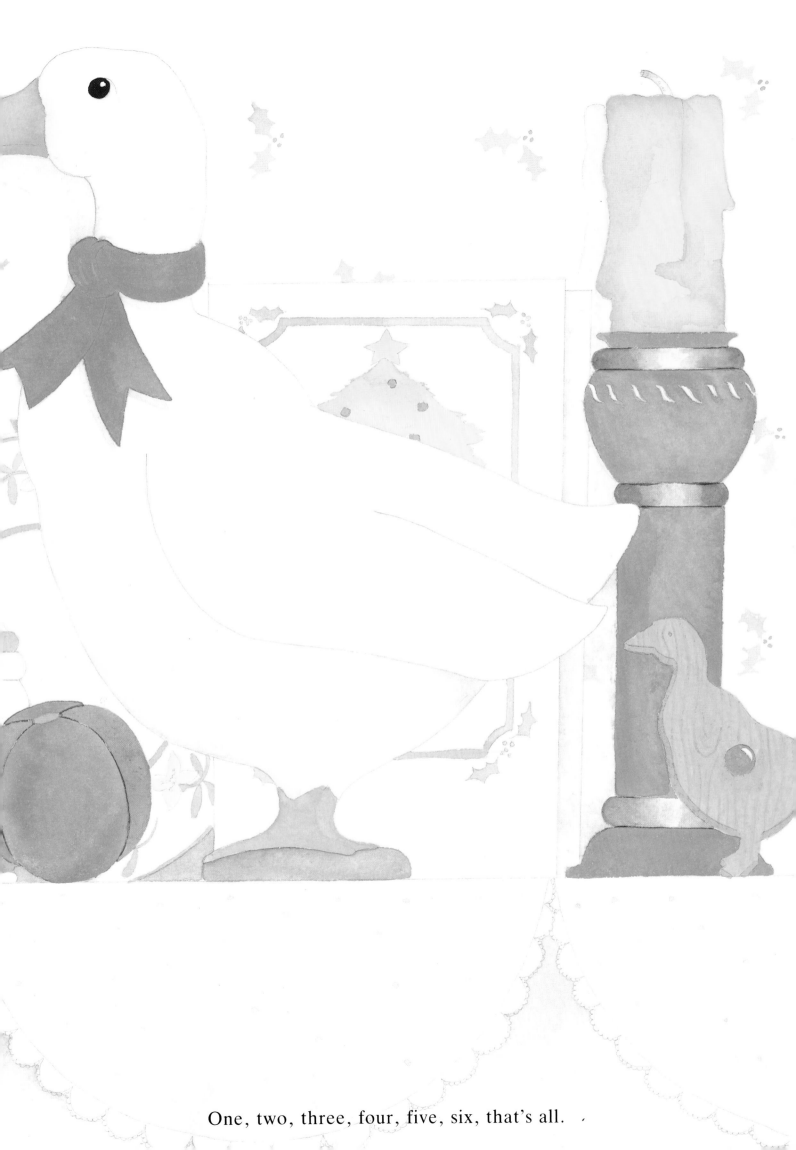

One, two, three, four, five, six, that's all.

Rabbit

Chester stares at the rabbits
His nose in the air,
Doesn't see Max the Cat or
That jigsaw piece there.

Furry rabbits, painted rabbits, rabbits galore,

First count to ten, then try counting more.

Piggy-Bank

"Will you tell me," says Chester
"Oh please, Piggy do,
Are you hiding a puzzle piece
Shaped just like you?"

There are not many flowers to count on the wall.

Only one, two, three, four, five, that's all.

Hen

Chester peeps from the bowl
All floury, and then
Sees that one of the eggs
Has turned into a hen!

Can you see one hen clucking high up on the wall?

In the rest of the picture count lots more in all.

Horse

Do you think little Chester
Who's so brave and strong,
Really knows that he's pulling
Two horses along?

How many horses can you see on the wall?

One horse, two and three, that's all.

Duck

There are too many ducks
Let's give Chester a clue
And ask him to look
Near the bubbly shampoo?

Now how many ducks can you find on the wall?

Then count all the other ducks, big and small.

Goat

Now, Chester, run faster,
Untangle your tail,
This goat has sharp horns and
Is hot on your trail.

Now count the daisies all yellow and white,

And if you find five, you've counted just right.

Cat

As Max peers from the shelf,
Chester searches below,
If you see the cat-piece
Then please do let them know.

See the bright orange cats around the plate,

If you count every one, you will reach up to eight.

Farmer

Chester clutches his head
All these spots hurt his eyes
So please help him look
For a man of small size.

How many spots can you see on the wall?

With Chester to help you, you might count them all.

Sheep

Chester really loves painting
The sheep in his book,
But he can't see the jigsaw,
Please help him to look.

Sheep on the floor and sheep on the wall,

Look very carefully and you might count them all.

Rooster

The rooster wakes early,
Crowing cock-a-doodle-do.
Will he help weary Chester
By giving him a clue?

Fat roosters, thin roosters, short and tall.

Two, four, six, eight, I think that's all.

Cow

Now our little mouse sees
Lots of cows going round.
Can you spot the strange one
That Chester has found?

If you count very carefully the cows on the plate,

I think you will find that they number just eight.

Turkey

Now Chester, look closely,
Underneath Turkey's wing,
No need to look further
Here's just the right thing!

How many turkeys can you count on the wall?

Just at the moment, none at all!

Dog

When our mouse pulls the string
Puppet jumps up and down,
But who's hiding the jigsaw,
The dog or the clown?

Now all the white spots on clown's bow-tie,

Add up to a lot, but give it a try!

Tree

Chester rides on the train
Just as proud as can be,
He is pointing his flag
At the puzzle piece tree!

Count all the trees carefully in the woods.

If you get the right number, that's very good!

Wheat

Chester balances here
On his little pink feet
Wondering where he can find
The right bundle of wheat.

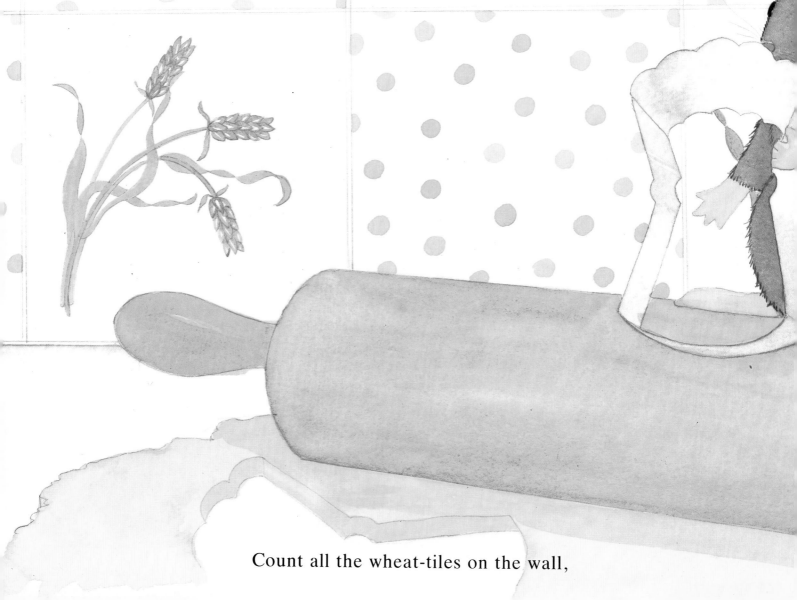

Count all the wheat-tiles on the wall,

FLOUR

One, two, three, four, five, that's all!

Fence

Jump the fence Chester, quick,
There's a rider behind,
But the small jigsaw-fence
Is much harder to find.

Four little horses on the wall,

Can you see one more, or is that all?

Scarecrow

Chester's making a scarecrow
And stuffs it with hay,
Where the right piece is hidden,
Is harder to say.

Two scarecrows with buttons, which one has more?

But look once again — what lies on the floor!

Donkey

Chester rides a toy donkey,
Let's hope he won't fall
Now he can't see the piece that
He looks for, at all.

How many boats can you see on the wall?

One, two, three, that's almost all.

Bee

Chester is hunting
A bee high and low,
Why don't you point out
The right way to go?

Busy bees, bumble bees, bees galore,

Two, four, six, eight, can you see more?

Egg-Basket

It's hard to see Chester,
Quite lost in the eggs,
"Oh please help me find the
Right basket," he begs.

How many yellow ribbons can you see?

I think you will count only one, two, three.

Bull

Chester meets a fierce bull
It gives him a scare,
But he has the piece safe,
Can you see it there?

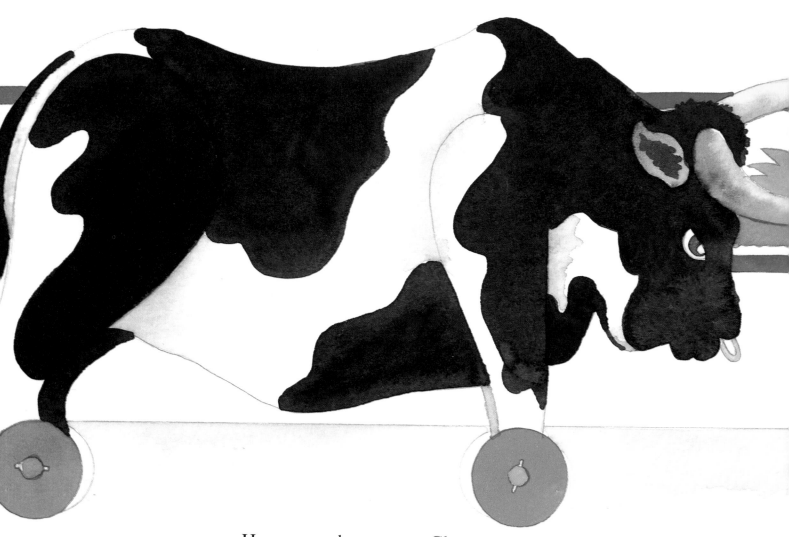

How many hooves on Chester's horse?

One, two, three, can you count any more?

Cart

Chester's found all the pieces
Except the last one
If you help him to find it,
You've finished – Well done!

How many spots can you see on the wall?

Then try counting the rest, both big and small.

Now here's our fine jigsaw
With pieces in place,
Chester is putting
The mouse in its space.
He wants to say "thank you"
For joining the fun,
For finding the pieces
And placing each one.
You've helped him to look for
The fence, dog and tree,
The eggs and the wheat and
That small wooden bee.
The goose, duck and rooster,
The horse, sheep and hen,
He hopes in the next book
You'll help him again.

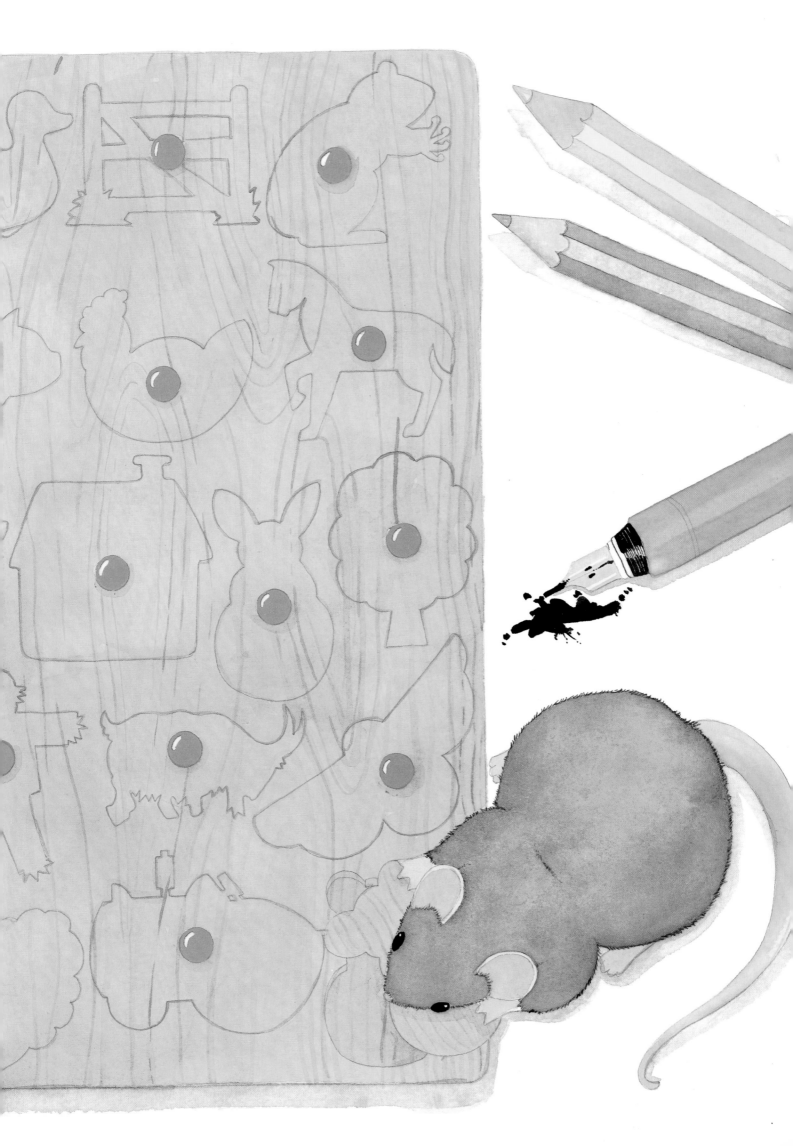